This is a work of fiction. Names, characters, places and incidents are either the
product of the author's imagination or, if real, are used fictitiously. All statements,
activities, stunts, descriptions, information and material of any other kind contained
herein are included for entertainment purposes only and should not be relied
on for accuracy or replicated as they may result in injury.

First published 2010 by Walker Books Ltd
87 Vauxhall Walk, London SE11 5HJ

2 4 6 8 10 9 7 5 3 1

Printed and bound in Italy

British Library Cataloguing in Publication Data:
a catalogue record for this book is available from the British Library

ISBN 978-1-4063-2051-0

www.walker.co.uk

www.andiwatson.biz

for
Gary

Among these unusual varieties there is an even more ancient and extraordinary tree.

It is the Butterworth Family Tree and it is said that when it blooms, relatives will grow.

Glister longed for relatives! She dreamed of a favourite uncle to come visit and do magic tricks, a cosseting aunt who'd knit her oversized jumpers and grandparents to shower her with gifts.

Since her father was so discouraging about their family, Glister had never told him that she'd stuck each of her baby teeth into the bark of the Family Tree over the years.

Thank your lucky stars that we'll never see fresh fruit from this tree again, its blooming days are over.

Because she'd swapped the bounty of the Tooth Fairy for a single wish, Glister knew that one day the Family Tree **would** bloom.

When she wasn't helping her father, Glister could be found in the Genealogy Room tidying the archives and gathering what information she could about her relations.

After everyone's morning routines were over, Glister set about getting to know the new arrivals.

Please, Miss, I beg of you, come no closer. The Phyllobius maculicornis* are abroad and my collection is in a most sorry state.

Oh, I can help.

Impossible, this is no place for a child.

Glister chose not to mention that she'd cared for the collection as best she could and if it hadn't been for her, perhaps they wouldn't have survived at all.

She left Appleton and decided to look in on Scotty instead.

He might well have been a hero on the guitar but he had much to learn in the art of polite conversation.

* Green Leaf weevil

He can't be expected to nursemaid you all day. And think of his situation, dragged from his own time. It'd be enough to make anyone melancholy.

But he has us, his family.

And we're here if he wants us.

Glister wasn't content to sit and wait, sifting through the family records, she hoped to find some mention of Charles Frederick, a friend, favoured dog, laundry list, anything at all to share with him.

But there was no mention of a Charles Frederick Butterworth.

She decided to search the portraits in the Long Gallery in the hope of locating a likeness.

HENRY
WYCHERLEY

Glister told herself
that of course there
was a likeness, they
were of the same
family.

But when Charles
himself walked
past the gallery,
she decided to
take a closer look.

Glister took her father to the Genealogy Room to demonstrate.

Here, "Henry Wycherley..."

CREAKKK

Chilblain doesn't sound to have fond memories of the name.

"... the youngest son did have a weakness for dice and games of hazard. The bailiffs did come to the gates of Chilblain Hall and take with them mahogany doors, carpets, crystal and silver in lieu of payment."

The cheek of him complaining how much better things were in his day. Where've the furniture and enamels gone?

Sold to pay his debts!

GROANNNN

Unfortunately, madam, I'm rather pre-occupied at the moment.

On the other hand, Butterworth loved giving tours of Chilblain, imagining himself to be the guide of a fine country residence.

This is a splendid example of a Lancashire low-back settle.

That was news to Glister as she'd dragged it out of a skip last summer.

Glister had assumed the novelty would wear off, that the sentient damp, falling ceiling plaster and frequent lack of running water would deter the guests.

However, Chilblain's reputation only grew and more tourists than ever arrived.

Glister wished she could gather her new relations and agree on a plan together. Then she wouldn't feel as though she was the only one who hadn't given up.

If only the Butterworths would pay attention to something beyond their own narrow interests.

Then Glister had an idea...

A row!

No one likes a barney as much as Acton and Fairfax.

Suddenly it was obvious. All along she should have played to the clan's cantankerousness and not to some pipe dream of happy families.

The first thing was to ask Eliza if she could have some of the wool spun from her flock's fur.

How much do you need?

How much have you got?

Within no time each of the Butterworths had their own piece of Chilblain Hall and wanted nothing to do with any of the others.

Henry arrived home to find Chilblain broken and his guests leaving in droves.

The adventure of a theme hotel had been taken a step too far, they wanted a full refund.

Finally, faced with cannon fire, Henry's drivers sensibly took to their heels.

It was the first time that the Butterworth brothers had agreed on anything for centuries.

Take flight y' scallywags!

Back to y'r ditches, lily-livers!

In the summer months the chalk giant was a magnet for butterflies and moths. Glister helped Appleton identify them and write the first newsletter of the Butterworth Entomological Society in several centuries.

The Butterworths, old and new, could occasionally be persuaded to gather together with a picnic under the Family Tree.

Henry Wycherley was much too busy working at his new jobs to attend picnics.

YAP YAP

Although she was often exasperated by her newly extended family, Glister had grown used to having them around.

If they had a limit to their time away from the Family Tree there was no sign of it. That suited Glister, she felt Chilblain Hall would be altogether too quiet without them.

Not that the occasional bit of quiet would be unwelcome.

THE BOWLING WEEVIL

Whose only known habitat is the holes in bowling balls.

×3

THE DOODLE BUG

Artistically talented Isopoda.

THE PHILATELY ROACH

Lives exclusively on the glue found on the back of postage stamps.

THE GREGOR SAMSA BEETLE

Lives in duvets and bed sheets and dreams of being a human.

×5

Appleton's Bug Collection

THE FUNNY MONEY SPIDER

Spins bank notes from its silk. Not considered legal currency inside the British Isles.

THE LONG - NOSED BEETLE

Often found in public places. Known to listen in on private conversations.

THE BUTTERWORTH BUNNY MITE

Can cause allergic reactions in some breeds.

THE NABOKOV OPENING BUTTERFLY

Distinctive markings resemble chess pieces.

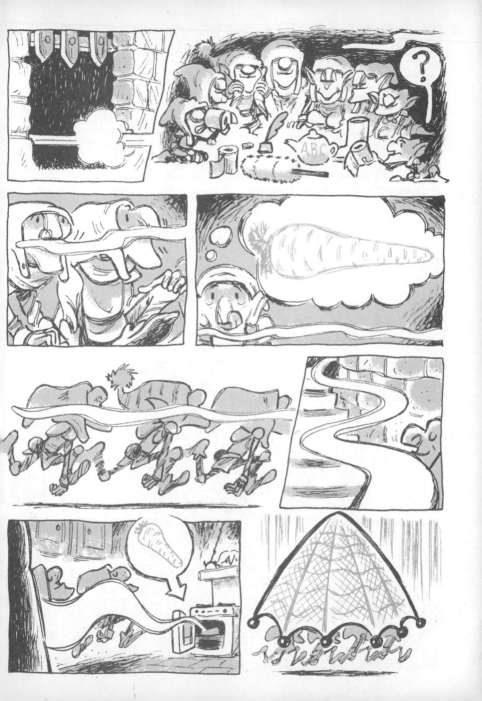

Thank you to...
Phil & Clara
mum & DAD
TA
Lizzie SPRATT
PATRick INSOLE
all the fine people at WALKER BOOKS
PAUL GRAVETT
ED HiLLYER
JAMiE S. RiCH
& all of you WONDERFUL READERS!

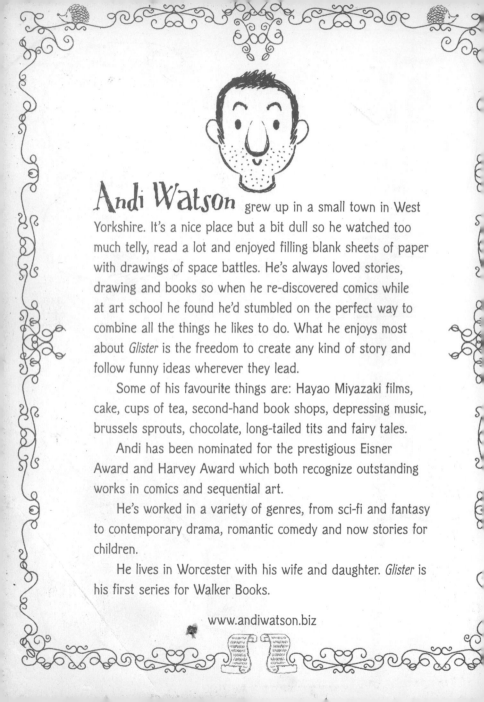

Andi Watson

grew up in a small town in West Yorkshire. It's a nice place but a bit dull so he watched too much telly, read a lot and enjoyed filling blank sheets of paper with drawings of space battles. He's always loved stories, drawing and books so when he re-discovered comics while at art school he found he'd stumbled on the perfect way to combine all the things he likes to do. What he enjoys most about *Glister* is the freedom to create any kind of story and follow funny ideas wherever they lead.

Some of his favourite things are: Hayao Miyazaki films, cake, cups of tea, second-hand book shops, depressing music, brussels sprouts, chocolate, long-tailed tits and fairy tales.

Andi has been nominated for the prestigious Eisner Award and Harvey Award which both recognize outstanding works in comics and sequential art.

He's worked in a variety of genres, from sci-fi and fantasy to contemporary drama, romantic comedy and now stories for children.

He lives in Worcester with his wife and daughter. *Glister* is his first series for Walker Books.

www.andiwatson.biz